DATE NIGHT FOR OLDIES

SILVEY-JEX

ISBN: 9781909732599

DATE NIGHT
FOR OLDIES

I must make an appointment with the dentist
FART
FART FART
FART
I should try the doctor first if I were you

How come your hair is the only thing that stands up in the morning?

Whoopee! Look at me.
SJ.

If I had that blokes money you know what I'd do?
Bugger all I imagine
PIZZA
PIZZA
SIVEWJEX

Ooohh!... up periscope

You've got a great body - what's your secret?
ARTIFICIAL LEGS
FALSE TEETH
PADDED BOTTOM
WIG
FALSE BOOBS
SJ.

SUPER
BOWLING

TEA DANCE
You're standing on my foot again.

Right old girl...lets burn some rubber
BANK
SJ.

Ooh... You are a naughty boy
DAD

BLOW UP DOLL
If you want me... I'll be in the woodshed
Alright... but mind what you're doing with that chopper of yours
SJ

BEST BEFORE
BEST BEFORE
BEST BEFORE
BEST BEFORE
SJ

It's no good Old Girl - we can't do it in one of these.

THE JACUZZI CO LTD

See... look, I'm not really pregnant- it was a joke.

SJ

Do you know every morning you say "Happy Birthday, have a nice cup of tea"
Well if I say it every morning I'll eventually get the right day won't I?
SILVEY-JEX

I'll be in bed...if youre up for it?

Okay, so where does a good looking, trendy, still fashionable, older man look for a pair of glasses?
His forehead?

Sitting around scratching myself is top of my "things to do" list.
SILVEY JEX

My husband and I sleep in sepevate beds. Mine is in London his is in Plymouth.

You're not supposed to wake up yet ... I'm not ready
SILVEY JEX

Basically I'm a very lazy person I'd like to explain the reasons why but I can't be bothered.

I think someone's creeping about downstairs... so STOP IT !!!

If I took all the hair from my nose and ears, and put it on my head - I wouldn't be so bald

I said... I'm gasping for a cup of tea
Yes. I ignored you the first time
SILVEY JEX.

Do you love me?
Who wants to know?
RACING POST

Hello dear I'm home
GOOD BYE DEAR I'VE GONE
SILVEY JEX.

Don't know about you-but I'm not interested in sex one little bit.
Well there's one little bit of me that's still very interested

If there is such a thing as re-incarnation -I'd like to come back as you my love.
Fine. Then perhaps you'll realize what I have to put up with

Oooh, that's a bit harsh I mean he is my husband
You ought to have him neutered

What is the point of going out? We're only going to end up back here again

Hello dear. Busy day? Supper's on the go.
LAP TOP

Forget it! you wouldn't know where to start
I'd know where to stop though

I'm going out with the dog.
What's she got that I haven't got?

What was the first thing that struck you when you met your wife?
Her handbag

Make love to me like there's no tomorrow
If I tried that there would be no Tomorrow

Let's do role reversal, you feign interest and I say "I've got a headache

Do you want to go out to eat tonight?
Yeh. Great. I won't be late back
SILVEY-JEX

Thought I'd do some online dating.
That'll be carbon dating will it?

Oh dear...
Viagra Falls
SILVEY JEX

SUNNY DAYS NUDIST CAMP
JOIN TODAY!
Are you excited about being a nudist?
Do I look excited?

Not only does he talk a load of it, but if it's there - he'll tread in it.
SILVEY-JEX

It's no good... I can't relax with your teeth grinning at me.

Generally, with wives - if you tell the truth, you don't have to remember anything.